# SUMMER SOLVED

# GRADE K–1
# ACTIVITY BOOK

Paving the Way from Kindergarten to 1st Grade
with Instruction on Math, Science, Reading,
Writing, Social Studies and More

This workbook belongs to

_____

_____

**Hi!**

Welcome to Summer Solved, the best workbook to help you move from Kindergarten to First Grade. In this workbook, you will find lots of fun activities to keep you busy and your brain sharp -- crossword puzzles, scavenger hunts, and much more. Work on a page or two each day, and answer keys are located in the back so you can check your work. When you've reached the end, you will find a certificate of completion to fill out. Show it off by hanging it in your room, on the refrigerator, or anywhere a grownup lets you!

Remember, use your imagination, get creative, and most importantly, **HAVE FUN!** Congratulations, First Grader!

# SUMMER READING BOOKS

- [ ] **Kevin Henkes -** Chrysanthemum
- [ ] **Oliver Jeffers -** The Day the Crayons Quit
- [ ] **Laura Numeroff -** If You Give a Mouse a Cookie
- [ ] **Maurice Sendak -** Where the Wild Things Are
- [ ] **Tedd Arnold -** Hi! Fly Guy
- [ ] **Arnold Lobel -** Frog and Toad are Friends
- [ ] **Marjorie Weinman Sharmat -** Nate the Great
- [ ] **Cynthia Rylant -** Henry and Mudge
- [ ] **John Klassen -** I Want My Hat Back
- [ ] **Carmen Tafolla -** What Can You Do with a Paleta?
- [ ] **Fran Manuskin -** Katie Woo and Friends
- [ ] **Jon Agee -** Life on Mars
- [ ] **Uma Krishnaswami -** Bright Sky, Starry City
- [ ] **Laura Marsh -** Caterpillar to Butterfly
- [ ] **Taeeun Yoo -** You are a Lion!: And Other Fun Yoga Poses
- [ ] **Kristin Baird Rattini -** National Geographic Readers: Weather
- [ ] **Katharine Kenah -** The Best Seat in First Grade

- [ ] **Corey R. Tabor -** Fox the Tiger
- [ ] **Sandra Markle -** Ranger Rick: I Wish I was an Orca
- [ ] **Michael Yu -** How to Catch a Monster

5

# SUMMER READING GOALS

My goal is to read ☐ books this summer.

I will read ☐ minutes every day.

My favorite place to read is ☐

### Books I want to read this summer:

_____

_____

_____

_____

_____

If the book you want to read isn't on the reading list, head to your local library!

If you find a book you like, find other books by the same author.

# MATH

**Add or subtract the units. Write your answer on the line.**

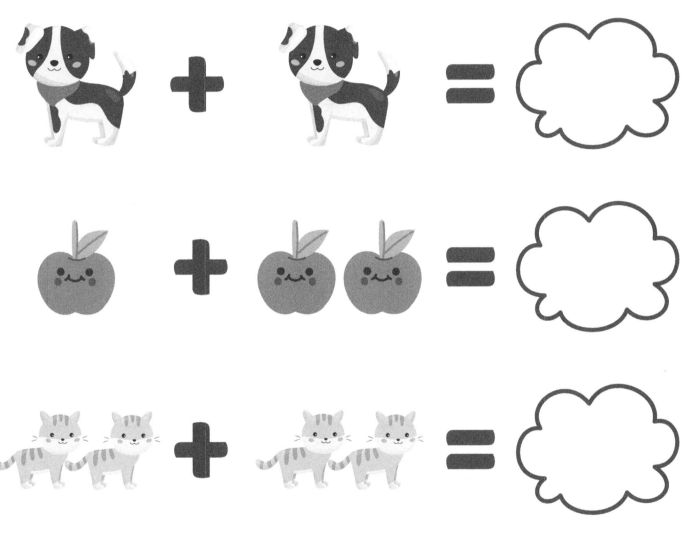

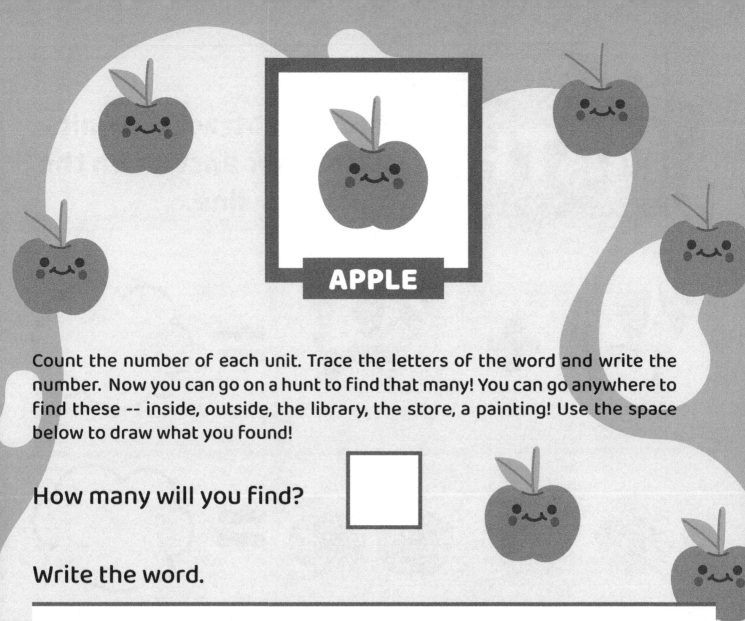

**APPLE**

Count the number of each unit. Trace the letters of the word and write the number. Now you can go on a hunt to find that many! You can go anywhere to find these -- inside, outside, the library, the store, a painting! Use the space below to draw what you found!

## How many will you find?

## Write the word.

- - - - - - - - - - - - - - - - - - - - - - - - - -

## Where will you find them?

| D | o |   |

| H | a |   |

| C |   | t |

|   | n | e |

| B |   | y |

| A |   | e |

| S | e |   |

| Y |   | s |

```
T E A C H E R I P Z
T D T R X L C G Y M
N D K W A L L Q R C
N B O O K J A O P P
L E A R N D S A E E
U L H X R M S N N D
N F R I E N D S C E
C K U R T Q A T I S
H U X L G J E R L K
U C U B O V I M R Q
```

**WORD BANK**

LEARN  GYM  CLASS  BOOK  FRIENDS

LUNCH  TEACHER  PENCIL  DESK

# DID YOU KNOW?

## ACROSS

2. This planet rotates backwards.
5. This woodland creature communicates with other animals by using its tail.
6. This President lost 5 elections before he won.
9. This is the only fruit with seeds on the outside.
10. Carrots were once only this color.

## DOWN

1. In the winter, this animal grows a beard.
3. She was the first woman in space!
4. This place only gets sunlight 182 days out of the year.
7. This planet has rings made of floating ice chunks.
8. This reflects sunlight, making them appear white.

## WORD BANK

SALLY RIDE    REINDEER    CLOUD    FOX    PURPLE

STRAWBERRY    VENUS    SATURN    SOUTH POLE    LINCOLN

# Egg in a Bottle

## INGREDIENTS

Hard boiled eggs (peeled)

Glass bottle (make sure opening is smaller than the egg)

Matches or lighter

Paper

Straw

## LESSON

## The power of pressure

!CAUTION! **Only do this experiment with an adult.**

## Instructions

1. Cut the paper long enough so that when it's fully inside the bottle, it stops just short of the opening.
2. Have an adult light the piece of paper and drop it inside the bottle.
3. Place the egg on the mouth of the bottle.
4. Note your observations on the next page.

## How it works

The air pressure inside the bottle and outside the bottle were the same. When you light the paper, the air inside the bottle heats up and starts to expand. Placing the egg on top of the bottle stops the expanded air from escaping. When the fire goes out, the air inside the bottle cools off and contracts, or shrinks. Now the air pressure outside the bottle is greater than inside, and it helps push the egg inside the bottle.

# Experiment Notes

Every good experiment, big or small, follows the same steps:

**1** Form a hypothesis  **2** Test your experiment  **3** Record your observations  **4** Test again -- and again!!

**What do I think will happen?**

_____

_____

_____

_____

**What actually happened? Test your experiment multiple times to see if you get the same result!**

_____

_____

_____

_____

# MATH

**Add or subtract the units. Write your answer on the line.**

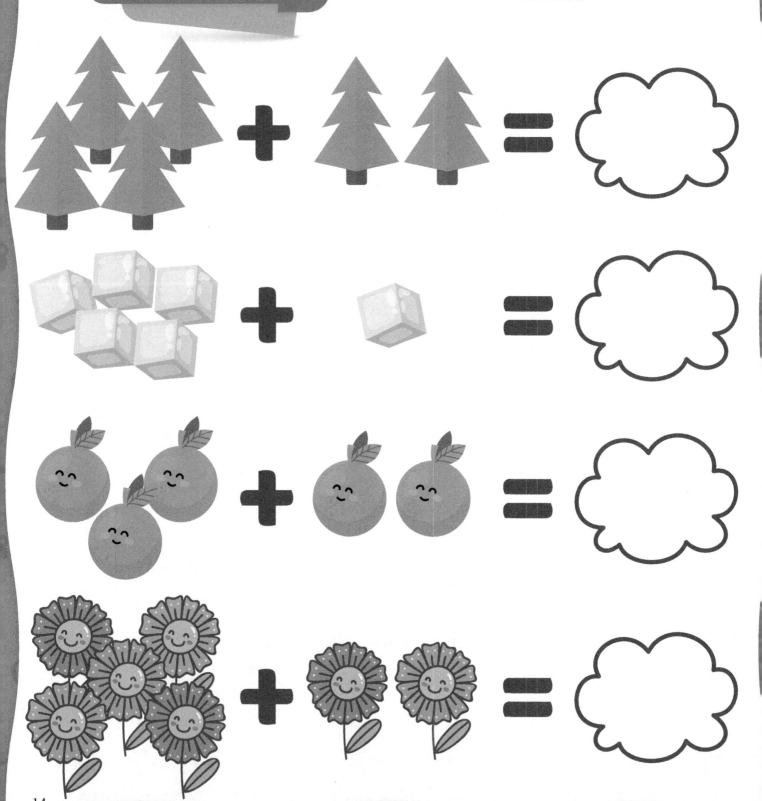

14

## FLOWER

Count the number of each unit. Trace the letters of the word and write the number. Now you can go on a hunt to find that many! You can go anywhere to find these -- inside, outside, the library, the store, a painting! Use the space below to draw what you found!

**How many will you find?**

**Write the word.**

- - - - - - - - - - - - - - - - - - - - - - - - - - - - - - - - - - - - -

**Where will you find them?**

- - - - - - - - - - - - - - - - - - - - - - - - - - - - - - - - - - - - - - - - - - - -

- - - - - - - - - - - - - - - - - - - - - - - - - - - - - - - - - - - - - - - - - - - -

- - - - - - - - - - - - - - - - - - - - - - - - - - - - - - - - - - - - - - - - - - - -

 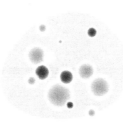  

- - - - - - - - - - - - - - - - - - - - - - - - - - - - - - - - - - - - - - - - - - - -

# FABULOUS FRUITS

```
V S I E Y M K L Y P C S D Q E M B
R C B Z B A N A N A L T S K O X G
X I P L N N N M X Q G R E C R O D
N E K N Q G Y Y Z S N A J M A H H
Y G D M J O T Y G W E W M X N A U
I M T V T W Z D F B A B K N G P H
B Y T N D E T K R R W E O V E L L
T L W D P E A C H F V R B D J Q V
E Z X L C S Z O H J G R Z R N D D
A K S J A R K P O S R Y X F C E D
I M F Y F N P W P T A S T T D X U
A F E H Y S X U T W P P I Q V B X
P X H V J H O K M N E E D K I W I
P K Y B E Q D U R X Y A U Z B Y U
L W F F M P O S H Y T R H C B R O
E Y P Q P I S I M C Q E P N E K O
E G J U K F U S O Z O T D W I C T
```

## WORD BANK

APPLE   STRAWBERRY   MANGO   KIWI   PEACH

BANANA   GRAPE   ORANGE   PEAR

# AWAY WE GO

**ACROSS**

4. This vehicle was invented in North Carolina by the Wright Brothers.
5. This transportation system runs underground
7. The original maximum speed of this transportation device was only about 2 miles per hour!

**DOWN**

1. This large transporter is yellow because yellow is so easy to spot.
2. Originally fueled by steam, this now runs off electricity or diesel fuel.
3. The Tour de France is a popular endurance race with riders using this.
6. This water vehicle has been around for thousands of years!

## WORD BANK

SCHOOL BUS    BICYCLE    BOAT    AIRPLANE    CAR    TRAIN    SUBWAY

# MATH

Add or subtract the units. Write your answer on the line.

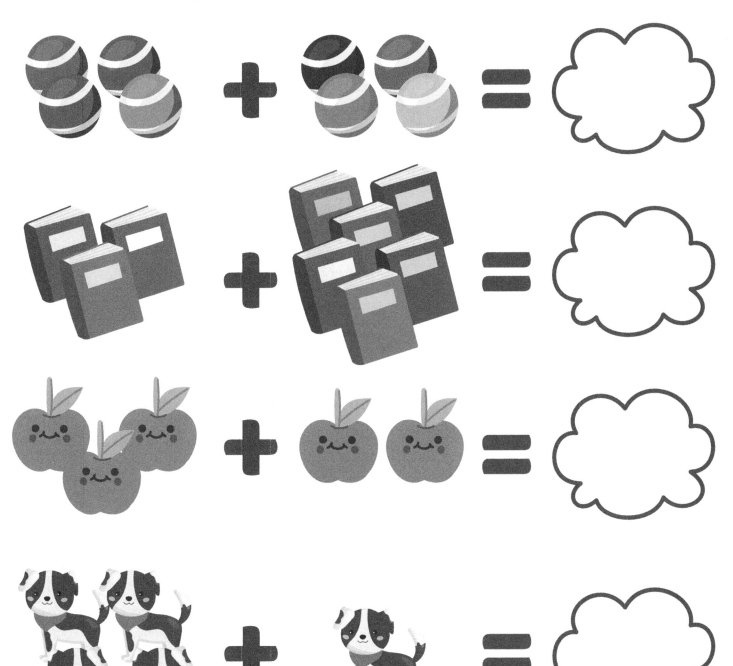

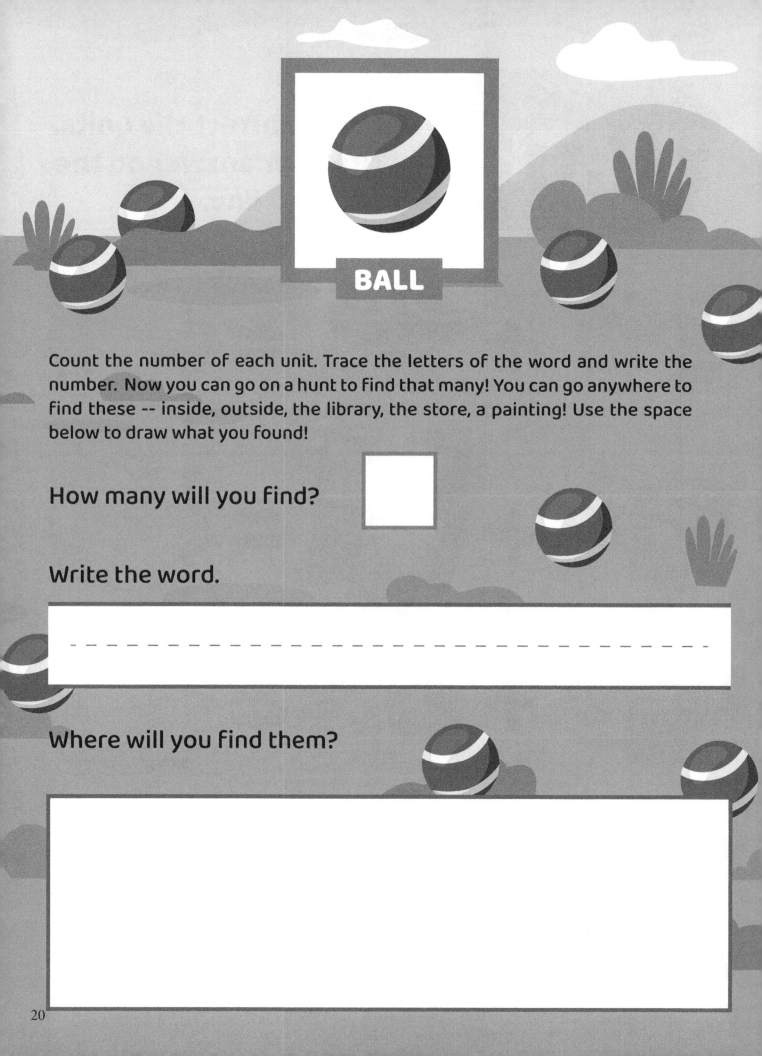

**BALL**

Count the number of each unit. Trace the letters of the word and write the number. Now you can go on a hunt to find that many! You can go anywhere to find these -- inside, outside, the library, the store, a painting! Use the space below to draw what you found!

## How many will you find?

## Write the word.

- - - - - - - - - - - - - - - - - - - - - - - - - - - - - - - - - - - - - - - - - -

## Where will you find them?

Say each sight word out loud. Fill in the missing letter

M o ⬜

H ⬜ P

B ⬜ x

⬜ o x

F ⬜ n

S ⬜ n

T w ⬜

H e ⬜

# HOW'S THE WEATHER

```
S F O G F E D F P K
T A P G Q Z S N O W
O N V U L S S P W Y
R A I N A U U C M F
M A L A T N J O E K
J Y D Q G N D L S U
G R I S O Y S D G L
H B W I N D M U E Z
O B B P Y M W C C B
T G C L O U D Y R C
```

## WORD BANK

CLOUDY   FOG   RAIN   STORM   WIND

COLD   HOT   SNOW   SUNNY

# EARTH'S CONTINENTS

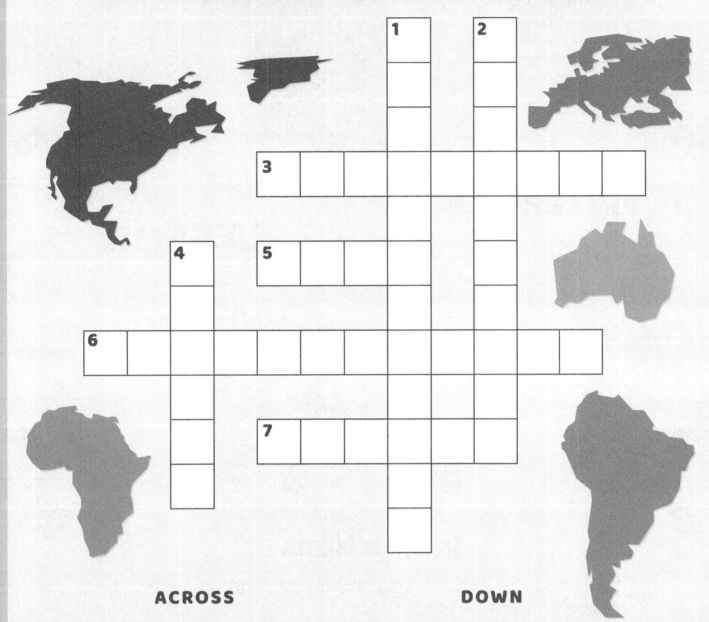

## ACROSS

3. Home of koalas and kangaroos.
5. The largest continent is home to 2/3 of the world's population.
6. Stretches from the Arctic Ocean to the Panama Canal.
7. Where the Earth's largest desert, the Sahara, is located.

## DOWN

1. The Amazon River runs through this continent.
2. This continent is ice cold!
4. The west cost of this continent is on the Atlantic ocean.

## WORD BANK

ANTARCTICA    AFRICA    EUROPE    ASIA

SOUTH AMERICA    AUSTRALIA    NORTH AMERICA

23

# Flip a Drawing

## MATERIALS

Glass of water

Paper

Marker

## LESSON

### Refraction

## Instructions

1. Draw something -- an arrow, a thumbs up, a cat -- just use your imagination!
2. Take a look at your drawing through the glass of water.
3. Record your observations on the next page. How does it look?
4. Try looking at your picture from different angles and distances. Note what you see each time.

## How it works

Refraction is the bending of light. When light passes through a material, it can bend or refract. In our experiment, light passes through the glass and water. But how does it flip an image? Light passes through the glass and water and bends toward a center focal point. Now the light rays cross each other. When they cross, what was on the left is now on the right; what was on the right is now on the left.

# Experiment Notes

Every good experiment, big or small, follows the same steps:

**1** Form a hypothesis

**2** Test your experiment

**3** Record your observations

**4** Test again -- and again!!

**What do I think will happen?**

_____

_____

_____

_____

**What actually happened? Test your experiment multiple times to see if you get the same result!**

_____

_____

_____

_____

# MATH

**Add or subtract the units. Write your answer on the line.**

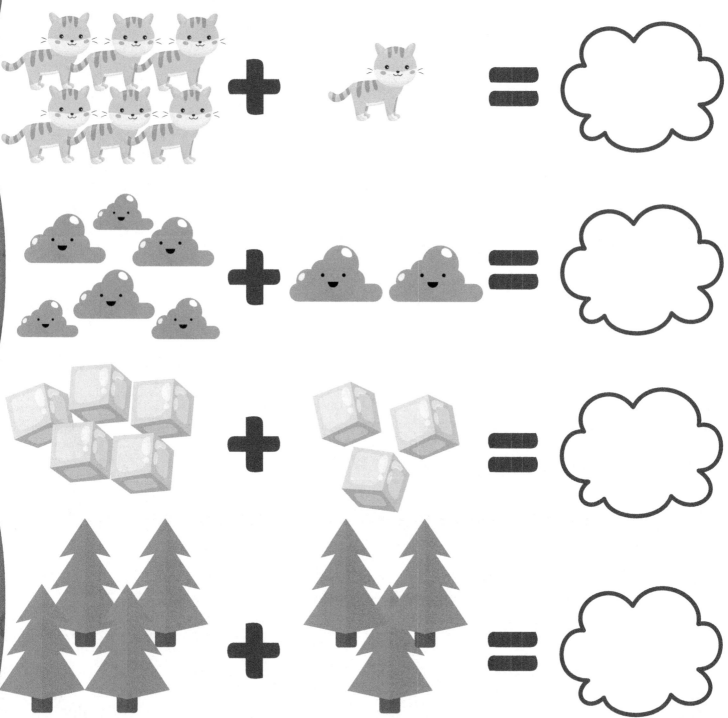

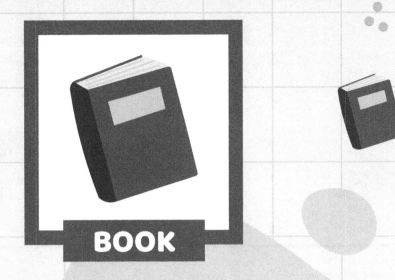

## BOOK

Count the number of each unit. Trace the letters of the word and write the number. Now you can go on a hunt to find that many! You can go anywhere to find these -- inside, outside, the library, the store, a painting! Use the space below to draw what you found!

**How many will you find?**

**Write the word.**

**Where will you find them?**

# Identify each picture, circle the words that rhyme.
## Write the rhyming words on the line.

- - - - - - - - - - - - - - - - - - - - - - - - - - - - - - - -

- - - - - - - - - - - - - - - - - - - - - - - - - - - - - - - -

- - - - - - - - - - - - - - - - - - - - - - - - - - - - - - - -

- - - - - - - - - - - - - - - - - - - - - - - - - - - - - - - -

# LET'S GO CAMPING

```
B M E T E N T M T H
N W P Q J X U E C X
A K Q Z K R C A M P
T S N A C K S N I W
U Q S M O R E S R O
R J Q R M L T Y F O
E Q R H A F R G Q D
W Z K I I I A U O S
L I H K F R I S U B
P E M E W E L J U U
```

## WORD BANK

CAMP   SNACKS   TRAIL   TENT   WOODS

FIRE   SMORES   NATURE   HIKE

# I CAN READ - SIGHT WORDS

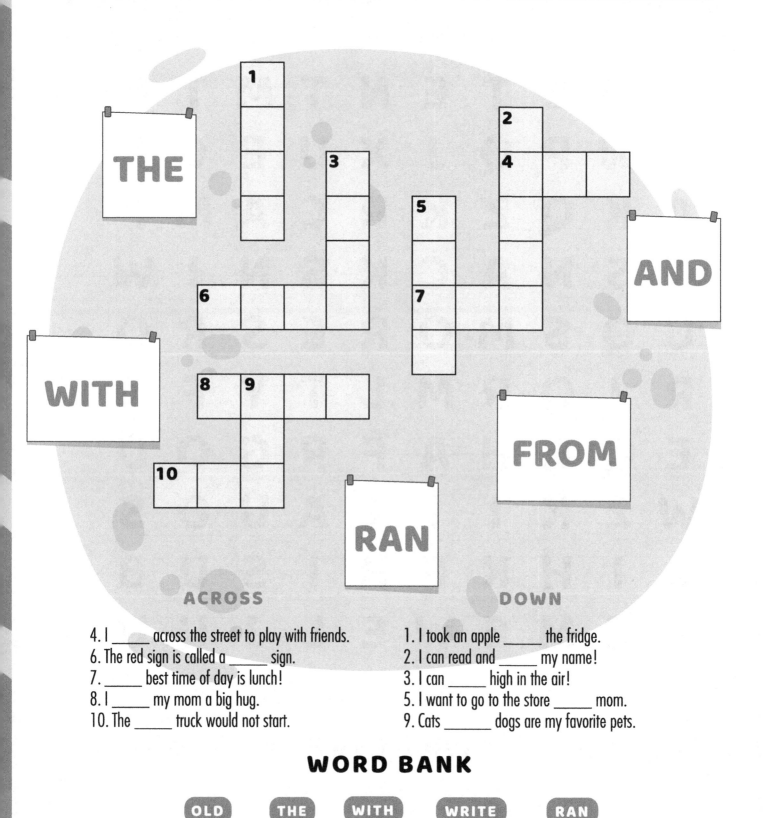

**ACROSS**

4. I _____ across the street to play with friends.
6. The red sign is called a _____ sign.
7. _____ best time of day is lunch!
8. I _____ my mom a big hug.
10. The _____ truck would not start.

**DOWN**

1. I took an apple _____ the fridge.
2. I can read and _____ my name!
3. I can _____ high in the air!
5. I want to go to the store _____ mom.
9. Cats _____ dogs are my favorite pets.

## WORD BANK

OLD   THE   WITH   WRITE   RAN

JUMP   GAVE   FROM   AND   STOP

**Add or subtract the units. Write your answer on the line.**

 −  =

 −  =

 −  =

 −  =

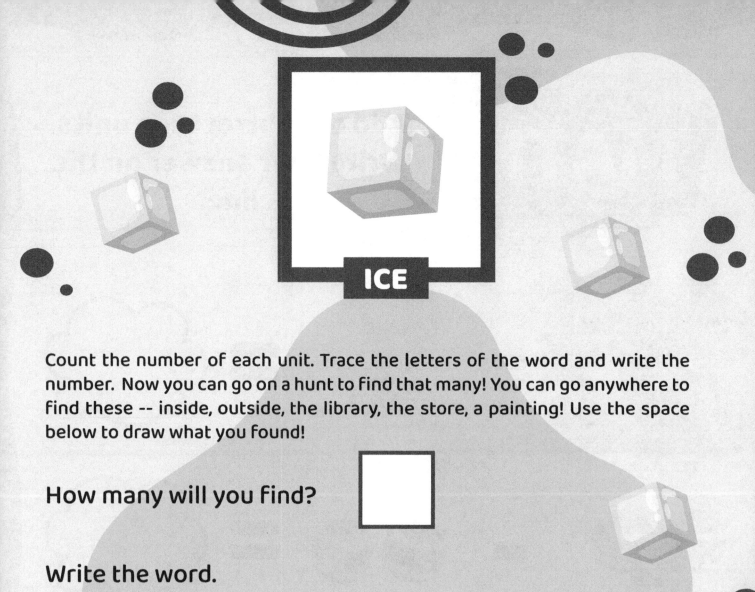

**ICE**

Count the number of each unit. Trace the letters of the word and write the number. Now you can go on a hunt to find that many! You can go anywhere to find these -- inside, outside, the library, the store, a painting! Use the space below to draw what you found!

## How many will you find?

## Write the word.

## Where will you find them?

Say each sight word out loud. Fill in the missing letter

| M | a | |
|---|---|---|

| A | | k |
|---|---|---|

| C | | p |
|---|---|---|

| | a | y |
|---|---|---|

| R | | n |
|---|---|---|

| A | | l |
|---|---|---|

| H | a | |
|---|---|---|

| | o | u |
|---|---|---|

# LETTUCE INTRODUCE THE VEGGIES

```
M G I W C B Y V D C U C U M B E R
Y P P Y G W P F L A S E V H T A V
H V Z L G B I L J I C U P B L G B
N B D H X P U L J B F I E U A Z X
J B E R G O W T A C E D P N W J E
I I B T D X Q K T M L I P M W T M
E C M A Y K O N I O N V E X L X F
U P O T A T O E S N P L R N Y Q Z
S R B E A N S V C D E Y S F P C Y
O Q S S Z C B U U K L M B B E B Y
H K F Y Q N R Z R V H C N R A Y I
N E F U U G O S I M G O J G S Q W
L F Q L L I C G A U D R L J U G Y
L L S C W H C I F N K N C V X K U
E V H F I F O Y A P O P D G L E Y
P L B H K U L I R O M Q B I J X B
X M C I L W I K M B C A R R O T S
```

## WORD BANK

ONION    BEANS    CORN    CUCUMBER    POTATOES

CARROTS    PEAS    BROCCOLI    PEPPERS

# PLANETS

**ACROSS**

4. Was once a planet, now a dwarf planet.
5. This is the smallest planet.
6. The hottest planet in our solar system.
8. It's bigger than any other planet.
9. This planet spins on its side.

**DOWN**

1. The only planet with life on it.
2. This planet is the furthest from the sun.
3. Also known as the red planet.
7. Most famous for its rings.

## WORD BANK

NEPTUNE    SATURN    MARS    EARTH    JUPITER

MERCURY    PLUTO    URANUS    VENUS

# Naked Eggs

## INGREDIENTS

Uncooked eggs

Jar

Vinegar

## LESSON

### Chemical reaction

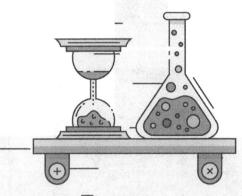

## Instructions

1. Fill a glass or jar with vinegar.
2. Carefully put your egg in the jar. Make sure there is enough vinegar to completely cover the egg. You might need to add a little more.
3. Wait for 12 hours. What do you see? Record your observation on the notes page.
4. Now wait for 2 whole days. You can use this time to work on other science experiments or read a book!
5. After 2 days, come back to your egg. Don't forget about it! Take the egg out of the jar and rinse well.
6. Note your observations.

## How it works

Eggshells are made of calcium carbonate, and vinegar contains a substance called acetic acid. When you combine the two, a chemical reaction occurs -- that reaction is those tiny bubbles you saw! Those bubbles are carbon dioxide. Slowly, the calcium carbonate and acetic acid will turn the entire eggshell into carbon dioxide until finally, you have your naked egg!

# Experiment Notes

Every good experiment, big or small, follows the same steps:

**1** Form a hypothesis  **2** Test your experiment  **3** Record your observations  **4** Test again -- and again!!

**What do I think will happen?**

_____

_____

_____

_____

**What actually happened? Test your experiment multiple times to see if you get the same result!**

_____

_____

_____

_____

# MATH

**Add or subtract the units. Write your answer on the line.**

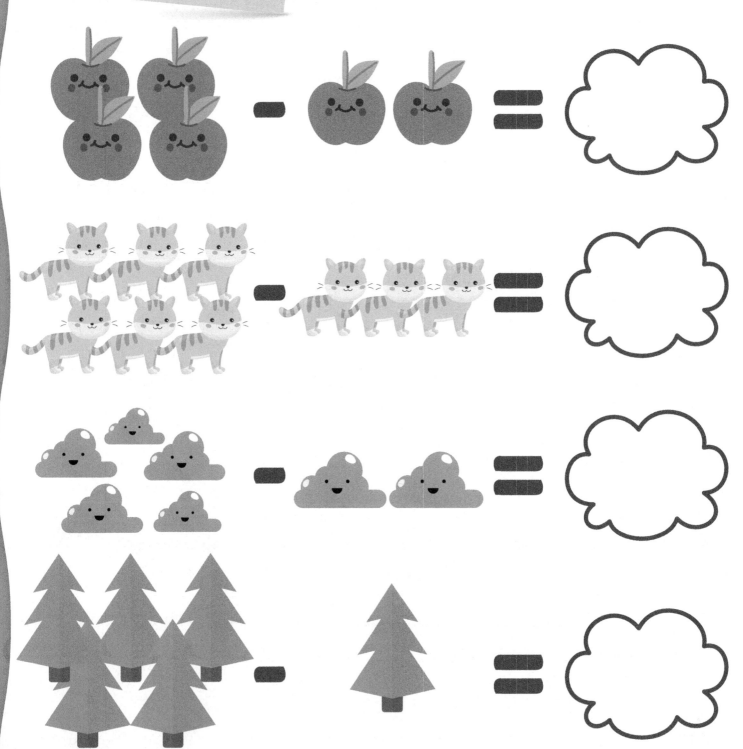

**CLOUD**

Count the number of each unit. Trace the letters of the word and write the number. Now you can go on a hunt to find that many! You can go anywhere to find these -- inside, outside, the library, the store, a painting! Use the space below to draw what you found!

## How many will you find?

## Write the word.

- - - - - - - - - - - - - - - - - - - - - - - - - - - - - - - - - - - - - - -

## Where will you find them?

Identify each picture, circle the words that rhyme.
Write the rhyming words on the line.

_____

- - - - - - - - - - - - - - - - - - - - - - - - - - - - - - - - - - - -

_____

_____

- - - - - - - - - - - - - - - - - - - - - - - - - - - - - - - - - - - -

_____

_____

- - - - - - - - - - - - - - - - - - - - - - - - - - - - - - - - - - - -

_____

_____

- - - - - - - - - - - - - - - - - - - - - - - - - - - - - - - - - - - -

_____

# MAN'S BEST FRIENDS

```
X Z O M M X L R F U J
L E N R N B G A S M
I J R A B B I T N O
Z T U R T L E E A U
A P F I F X B Q K S
R B B D I N W Y E E
D Y I O S Y B V U P
V O R L H D C A T P
O N D B U O N V G V
N N R K B G O H Q I
```

WORD BANK

LIZARD    MOUSE    TURTLE    RABBIT

DOG    BIRD    CAT    FISH

# PLAY BALL!

## ACROSS

2. This ball goes BUMP, SET, SPIKE over the net.
5. Athletes use a balance beam.
6. Played with racket and yellow ball.
7. Typically has 18 holes on the course.
8. This ball is orange and played on a court.

## DOWN

1. Uses a puck instead of a ball.
3. Played with a bat and ball.
4. Uses a bow and arrow.

## WORD BANK

VOLLEYBALL · GOLF · BASKETBALL · GYMNASTICS

HOCKEY · BASEBALL · ARCHERY · TENNIS

# MORE OR LESS

## Which group has more?

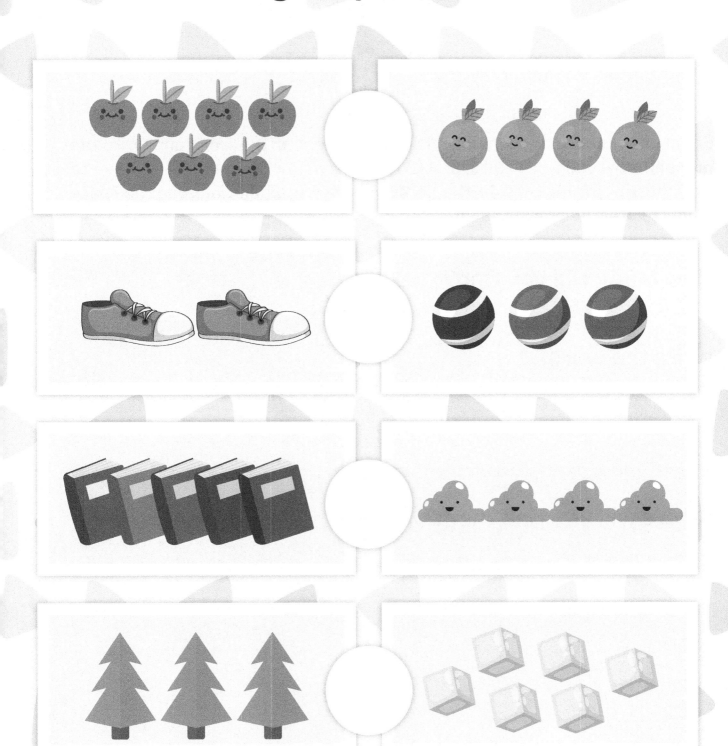

**LEAF**

Count the number of each unit. Trace the letters of the word and write the number. Now you can go on a hunt to find that many! You can go anywhere to find these -- inside, outside, the library, the store, a painting! Use the space below to draw what you found!

## How many will you find?

## Write the word.

## Where will you find them?

Say each sight word out loud. Fill in the missing letter

| H | | w |
|---|---|---|

| C | | r |
|---|---|---|

| | i | g |
|---|---|---|

| | e | n |
|---|---|---|

| | e | w |
|---|---|---|

| | i | x |
|---|---|---|

| C | a | |
|---|---|---|

| | w | l |
|---|---|---|

# ON THE FARM

```
B O Z P G D F T R C G J X X I V W
F W W J W T L H I A W K H P S M X
M C M R C M Z W S X E T A B C F T
F S H E X N D N Q B K G B L P R E
N L U U C P G G Z C A G S U Z H Z
U M I J G L H S Q H T L O T O M U
P B D U V B A R N I H T V T T D P
V I G P C Q Q R G C M R F E N C E
I Q L T B X W I J K T A E N U A K
D P F Q H D D J F E F C M T P F S
M I B R A F H L M N H T O A J T A
M G E S Y S J W E O P O N X I X G
D G H S M N S A E F A R M E R G R
L L H B Q E B T S T J W G L E E A
U X M B D F C H V B M X P S I P I
Z T W M X Z Z E J V A P O L R E N
P F T U E N Y F Z W C O W Q V W O
```

## WORD BANK

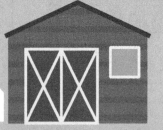

FENCE   PIG   TRACTOR

CHICKEN   COW   BARN   GRAIN   FARMER   HAY

# U.S. PRESIDENTS

## ACROSS

3. He kept a flock of sheep at the White House.
4. He was a radio announcer for the Chicago Cubs.
7. This President had a stamp collection.
8. He was the tallest President.
9. This man was the first left-handed President.
10. The only President who studied to become a medical doctor.

## DOWN

1. This President's wife started the first White House Library.
2. First President of the United States.
5. First President to live in the White House.
6. He was the first President that was a Boy Scout.

## WORD BANK

HARRISON   LINCOLN   ADAMS   WASHINGTON   ROOSEVELT

REAGAN   FILLMORE   GARFIELD   KENNEDY   WILSON

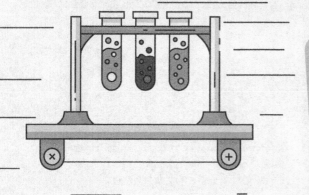

# Stand on a Paper Cup

## MATERIALS

Paper cups

Cardboard box, cut into large squares

## LESSON

## Physics and engineering

## Instructions

1. Stand on a single paper cup. Record what happens.
2. Arrange 6 paper cups so they are evenly spaced. Place a sheet of cardboard on top of the cups. Try to stand on top. What happens?
3. Arrange more paper cups, evenly spaced. Place the cardboard on top, and then stand on it. What happens now?
4. Try different numbers of cups, and space them farther or closer together.
5. Does the number of cups and the amount of space between them make a difference?

## How it works

When you stand on a single paper cup, all of your weight crushes the cup. But when you add more cups and a cardboard top, your weight can be divided evenly among each cup. The more cups you add, the less weight each cup has to hold.

# Experiment Notes

Every good experiment, big or small, follows the same steps:

**1** Form a hypothesis

**2** Test your experiment

**3** Record your observations

**4** Test again -- and again!!

**What do I think will happen?**

**What actually happened? Test your experiment multiple times to see if you get the same result!**

# MORE OR LESS

## Which group has more?

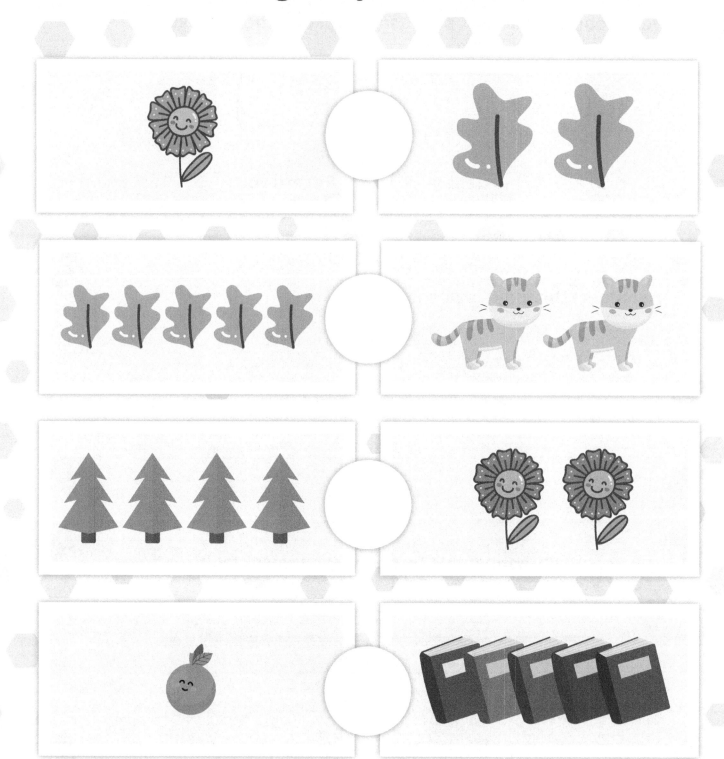

## SHOE

Count the number of each unit. Trace the letters of the word and write the number. Now you can go on a hunt to find that many! You can go anywhere to find these -- inside, outside, the library, the store, a painting! Use the space below to draw what you found!

## How many will you find?

## Write the word.

- - - - - - - - - - - - - - - - - - - - - - - - - - - - - - - - - - - - - - - - - - - - - -

## Where will you find them?

# Identify each picture, circle the words that rhyme.
## Write the rhyming words on the line.

- - - - - - - - - - - - - - - - - - - - - - - - - - - - - - - - - - - - - - - - - -

- - - - - - - - - - - - - - - - - - - - - - - - - - - - - - - - - - - - - - - - - -

- - - - - - - - - - - - - - - - - - - - - - - - - - - - - - - - - - - - - - - - - -

- - - - - - - - - - - - - - - - - - - - - - - - - - - - - - - - - - - - - - - - - -

# OUTER SPACE

```
N R S M E T E O R M
G A S T R O N A U T
R C X B S S M R Y K
A A G N P A S T A R
V M U L A O K S U N
I O W J C X I H N M
T O H N E X H E Y Z
Y N O R O C K E T V
X D P L A N E T S E
U R W F K O F R Z A
```

## WORD BANK

ASTRONAUT  METEOR  PLANETS  SPACE  SUN

GRAVITY  MOON  ROCKET  STAR

# UNDER THE SEA

## ACROSS

3. One species of this mammal is the largest animal on Earth!
4. The unicorn of the sea is a species of whale!
8. This fur-covered sea animal has four flippers.
9. This reptile lays eggs on land but lives in water.

## DOWN

1. This sea mammal lives in a group called a pod and uses echolocation like bats!
2. This fish has no bones and can live up to 150 years!
5. This crustacean has five pairs of legs, including claws!
6. The Great Barrier Reef is made of this.
7. This eight-armed creature does not have a backbone!

 WORD BANK

WHALE   SQUID   SEAL   LOBSTER   DOLPHIN

NARWHAL   SHARK   TURTLE   CORAL

# MORE OR LESS

## Which group has more?

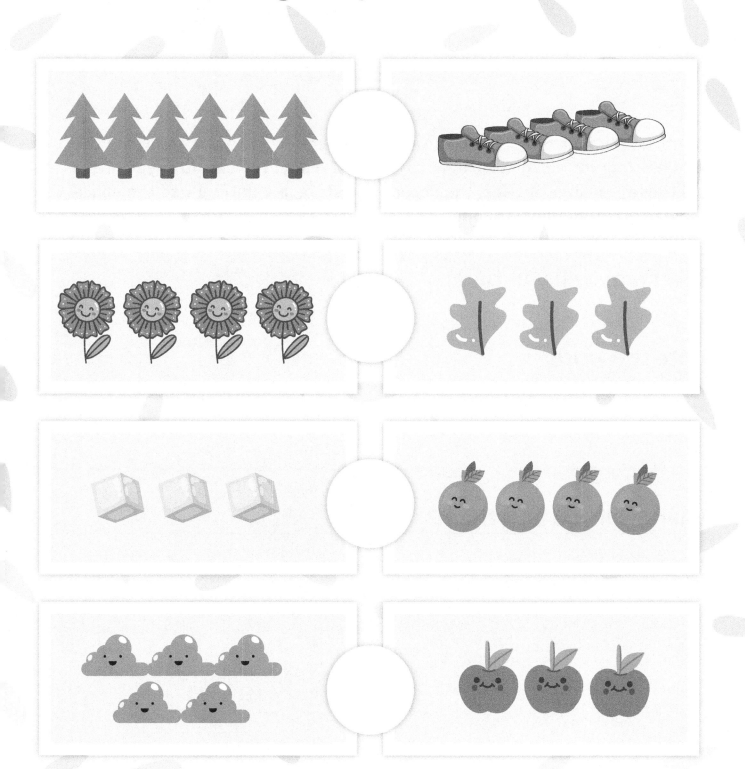

**ORANGE**

Count the number of each unit. Trace the letters of the word and write the number. Now you can go on a hunt to find that many! You can go anywhere to find these -- inside, outside, the library, the store, a painting! Use the space below to draw what you found!

## How many will you find?

## Write the word.

- - - - - - - - - - - - - - - - - - - - - - - - - - - - - - - - - - - - -

## Where will you find them?

Identify each picture, circle the words that rhyme.
Write the rhyming words on the line.

- - - - - - - - - - - - - - - - - - - - - - - - - - - - - - - - - - - -

- - - - - - - - - - - - - - - - - - - - - - - - - - - - - - - - - - - -

- - - - - - - - - - - - - - - - - - - - - - - - - - - - - - - - - - - -

- - - - - - - - - - - - - - - - - - - - - - - - - - - - - - - - - - - -

# SUMMER FUN

```
O U W B F M R G T R K L W W R Q S
U R Y I L V E J Q S W I M C I K Y
T S H T E R Q V N I Z E G C S K V
S A C L M D L J P N Z T B N H G V
I L U H O S A N D A L S B Y O O F
D D G F N N N D T D X L A S R U P
E T R P A X M G W T X I E F T U T
K D V N D W O J E C G W A F S N C
Y Z P D E W K D I A Z U K A H L S
W H P A R K H H U Z N C R X J Z X
S X H S U P O P S I C L E I X O S
Q N L O E F N Z C A F D T P K V V
T J V A C A T I O N J Z K L U N Q
H J X A K V V U E F W Y D V Q Y T
O S G J L X U J E X P L O R E B E
N D Y T Y E Q Q I C B K C T P I H
C S L B H K R L H X I U K S V S C
```

## WORD BANK

PARK   POPSICLE   SHORTS   LEMONADE   SWIM

SANDALS   OUTSIDE   VACATION   EXPLORE

# WE WALK ON LAND

## ACROSS

2. This animal is the ancestor of our modern dog.
5. This striped animal is closely related to the horse and lives in Africa.
6. Also known as the king of the jungle, this animal's roar can be heard up to five miles away!
7. The teeth on this small animal never stop growing.
9. This is the second-largest animal that lives on land.
10. This animal is known for its long neck.

## DOWN

1. This fun animal has opposable thumbs, just like us!
3. This species looks white, but its fur is actually transparent!
4. Native to Australia, this land animal has large feet that help it jump.
8. This striped animal is surprisingly a great swimmer!

## WORD BANK

MONKEY    POLAR BEAR    GIRAFFE

ZEBRA    HIPPO    KANGAROO    TIGER    LION    WOLF    RABBIT

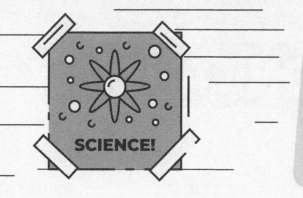

# Weather in a Bag

## INGREDIENTS

Gallon-size baggie

Water

Food dye (blue works great!)

Permanent marker

Packing tape

Window

## LESSON

### Weather

## Instructions

1. Pour approximately 2-3 inches of water in your baggie.
2. Add several drops of food coloring to the water.
3. Close the baggie completely. You can tape it to be double sure.
4. Tape the bag to a window. Make sure there's plenty of sunlight!
5. Now you'll have to wait. Every hour, come back and record what's happening.

## How it works

The sun heats the water in the bag, turning it into a gas. This is called evaporation. The water then hits the sides of the bag and begins to cool, turning back into a liquid. That process is called condensation. The water drops grow larger and heavier, and eventually will start to fall back into the bottom of the bag -- rain. The cycle continues.

# Experiment Notes

Every good experiment, big or small, follows the same steps:

**1** Form a hypothesis  **2** Test your experiment  **3** Record your observations  **4** Test again -- and again!!

**What do I think will happen?**

_____

_____

_____

_____

**What actually happened? Test your experiment multiple times to see if you get the same result!**

_____

_____

_____

_____

# MORE OR LESS

## Which group has more?

## TREE

Count the number of each unit. Trace the letters of the word and write the number. Now you can go on a hunt to find that many! You can go anywhere to find these -- inside, outside, the library, the store, a painting! Use the space below to draw what you found!

## How many will you find?

## Write the word.

## Where will you find them?

# U.S. STATES

```
C A L I F O R N I A
K O B A L C O A H R
F B T P O N H L L H
T J U K R E I E S A
E Q K O I H O H J W
X B J P D E E F O A
A K A L A S K A K I
S R I K A N S A S I
A R I Z O N A S W U
W V N E W Y O R K I
```

## WORD BANK

ALASKA     CALIFORNIA     HAWAII     NEW YORK     TEXAS

ARIZONA     FLORIDA     KANSAS     OHIO

# READING IS FUN - SIGHT WORDS

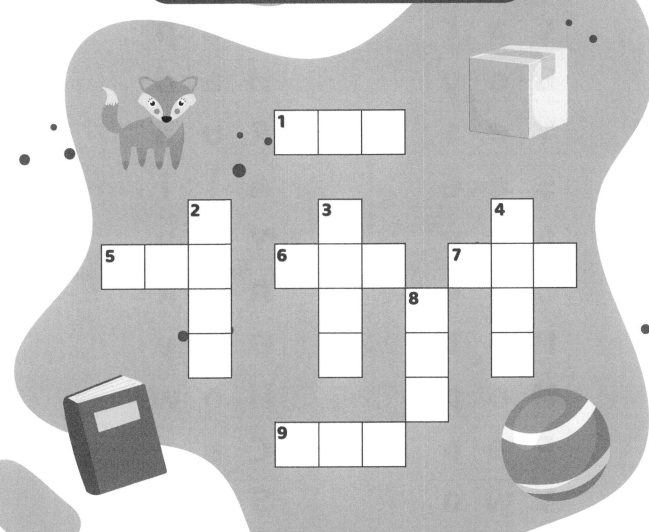

## ACROSS

1. We had _____ at the park today.
5. I can _____ with my eyes.
6. My _____ is gray with black stripes.
7. The _____ is red and white.
9. The little bunny likes to _____ in the yard.

## DOWN

2. I like to _____ in the library.
3. My favorite beach toy is a beach _____.
4. The boy read his _____ after class.
8. Think outside the _____.

## WORD BANK

BOX   SEE   BOOK   HOP   CAT   READ   FUN   BALL   FOX

# ANSWER KEY

| D | o | g |
|---|---|---|
| C | a | t |
| B | o | y |
| Y | e | s |
| S | e | e |
| A | t | e |
| O | n | e |
| H | a | t |
| M | o | p |
| F | a | n |
| T | w | o |
| S | u | n |
| H | o | p |
| F | o | x |
| B | o | x |
| H | e | r |

| M | a | p |
|---|---|---|
| C | a | p |
| H | a | d |
| R | u | n |
| A | l | l |
| Y | o | u |
| A | s | k |
| D | a | y |
| H | o | w |
| C | a | r |
| S | i | x |
| O | w | l |
| N | e | w |
| C | a | p |
| H | e | n |
| P | i | g |

| | |
|---|---|
| 1+1=2 | More: |
| 1+2=3 | 6 |
| 2+2=4 | 4 |
| 1+3=4 | 4 |
| | 5 |
| 4+2=6 | |
| 5+1=6 | More: |
| 3+2=5 | 6 |
| 5+2=7 | 7 |
| | 6 |
| 4+4=8 | 7 |
| 3+6=9 | |
| 3+2=5 | Rhyme: |
| 4+1=5 | Cat - hat, bat |
| | Boy - toy |
| 6+1=7 | Book - hook, look |
| 6+2=8 | Old - mold, cold |
| 5+3=8 | |
| 4+3=7 | Rhyme: |
| | Car - jar |
| 6-1=5 | House- mouse |
| 3-2=1 | Coat - boat |
| 4-3=1 | Red - bed |
| 5-5=0 | |
| | Rhyme: |
| 4-2=2 | Box - fox, socks |
| 6-3=3 | Tree - knee, ski |
| 5-2=3 | Log - dog, frog |
| 5-1=4 | Girl - curl, swirl |
| | |
| More: | Rhyme: |
| 7 | Four - door |
| 3 | Big - pig |
| 5 | Bus - plus |
| 6 | Sun - run |
| | |
| More: | Rhyme: |
| 2 | Map - cap |
| 5 | Mug - bug |
| 4 | Rain - train, plane |
| 5 | Star - car |

## Away We Go!

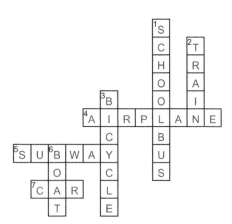

**Across**
4. This vehicle was invented in North Carolina by the Wright Brothers.
5. This transportation system runs underground.
7. The original maximum speed of this transportation device was only about 2 miles per hour!

**Down**
1. This large transporter is yellow because yellow is so easy to spot.
2. Originally fueled by steam, this now runs off electricity or diesel fuel.
3. The Tour de France is a popular endurance race with riders using this.
6. This water vehicle has been around for thousands of years!

**Word Bank**

| | | | |
|---|---|---|---|
| Bicycle | Boat | Car | Train |
| Airplane | School Bus | Subway | |

## Did You Know?

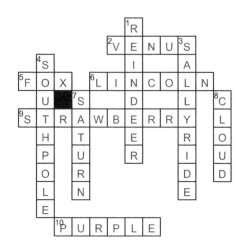

**Across**
2. This planet rotates backwards.
5. This woodland creature communicates with other animals by using its tail.
6. This President lost 5 elections before he won.
9. This is the only fruit with seeds on the outside.
10. Carrots were once only this color.

**Down**
1. In the winter, this animal grows a beard.
3. She was the first woman in space!
4. This place only gets sunlight 182 days out of the year.
7. This planet has rings made of floating ice chunks.
8. This reflects sunlight, making them appear white.

**Word Bank**

| | | | |
|---|---|---|---|
| Lincoln | Reindeer | Sally Ride | Saturn |
| Fox | South Pole | Cloud | Venus |
| Purple | Strawberry | | |

## Back to School

```
T  E  A  C  H  E  R  I  P  Z
T  D  T  R  X  L  C  G  Y  M
N  D  K  W  A  L  L  Q  R  C
N  B  O  O  K  J  A  O  P  P
L  E  A  R  N  D  S  A  E  E
U  L  H  X  R  M  S  N  N  D
N  F  R  I  E  N  D  S  C  E
C  K  U  R  T  Q  A  T  I  S
H  U  X  L  G  J  E  R  L  K
U  C  U  B  O  V  I  M  R  Q
```

Learn   Friends   Gym   Lunch   Class   Teacher   Book   Pencil   Desk

## Fabulous Fruits

```
V  S  I  E  Y  M  K  L  Y  P  C  S  D  Q  E  M  B
R  C  B  Z  B  A  N  A  N  A  L  T  S  K  O  X  G
X  I  P  L  N  N  N  M  X  Q  G  R  E  C  R  O  D
N  E  K  N  Q  G  Y  Y  Z  S  N  A  J  M  A  H  H
Y  G  D  M  J  O  T  Y  G  W  E  W  M  X  N  A  U
I  M  T  V  T  W  Z  D  F  B  A  B  K  N  G  P  H
B  Y  T  N  D  E  T  K  R  R  W  E  O  V  E  L  L
T  L  W  D  P  E  A  C  H  F  V  R  B  D  J  Q  V
E  Z  X  L  C  S  Z  O  H  J  G  R  Z  R  N  D  D
A  K  S  J  A  R  K  P  O  S  R  Y  X  F  C  E  D
I  M  F  Y  F  N  P  W  P  T  A  S  T  T  D  X  U
A  F  E  H  Y  S  X  U  T  W  P  P  I  Q  V  B  X
P  X  H  V  J  H  O  K  M  N  E  E  D  K  I  W  I
P  K  Y  B  E  Q  D  U  R  X  Y  A  U  Z  B  Y  U
L  W  F  F  M  P  O  S  H  Y  T  R  H  C  B  R  O
E  Y  P  Q  P  I  S  I  M  C  Q  E  P  N  E  K  O
E  G  J  U  K  F  U  S  O  Z  O  T  D  W  I  C  T
```

Apple   Banana   Grape   Kiwi   Mango   Orange   Peach   Pear   Strawberry

## Earth's Continents

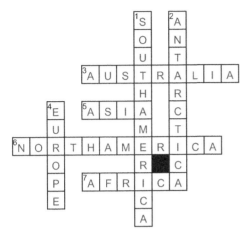

**Across**
3. Home of koalas and kangaroos.
5. The largest continent is home to 2/3 of the world's population.
6. Stretches from the Arctic Ocean to the Panama Canal.
7. Where the Earth's largest desert, the Sahara, is located.

**Down**
1. The Amazon River runs through this continent.
2. This continent is ice cold!
4. The west cost of this continent is on the Atlantic ocean.

**Word Bank**

| | | | |
|---|---|---|---|
| North America | Australia | Africa | South America |
| Asia | Europe | Antarctica | |

## I Can Read - Sight Words

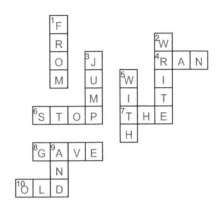

**Across**
4. I ____ across the street to play with friends.
6. The red sign is called a ____ sign.
7. ____ best time of day is lunch!
8. I ____ my mom a big hug.
10. The ____ truck would not start.

**Down**
1. I took an apple ____ the fridge.
2. I can read and ____ my name!
3. I can ____ high in the air!
5. I want to go to the store ____ mom.
9. Cats ____ dogs are my favorite pets.

**Word Bank**

| | | | |
|---|---|---|---|
| Write | The | Jump | From |
| Stop | And | With | Gave |
| Ran | Old | | |

## How's The Weather

```
S  F  O  G  F  E  D  F  P  K
T  A  P  G  Q  Z  S  N  O  W
O  N  V  U  L  S  S  P  W  Y
R  A  I  N  A  U  U  C  M  F
M  A  L  A  T  N  J  O  E  K
J  Y  D  Q  G  N  D  L  S  U
G  R  I  S  O  Y  S  D  G  L
H  B  W  I  N  D  M  U  E  Z
O  B  B  P  Y  M  W  C  C  B
T  G  C  L  O  U  D  Y  R  C
```

Cloudy  Cold  Fog  Hot  Rain  Snow  Storm  Sunny  Wind

## Let's Go Camping

```
B  M  E  T  E  N  T  M  T  H
N  W  P  Q  J  X  U  E  C  X
A  K  Q  Z  K  R  C  A  M  P
T  S  N  A  C  K  S  N  I  W
U  Q  S  M  O  R  E  S  R  O
R  J  Q  R  M  L  T  Y  F  O
E  Q  R  H  A  F  R  G  Q  D
W  Z  K  I  I  A  U  O  S
L  I  H  K  F  R  I  S  U  B
P  E  M  E  W  E  L  J  U  U
```

Camp  Fire  Hike  Nature  Smores  Snacks  Tent  Trail
Woods

# Planets

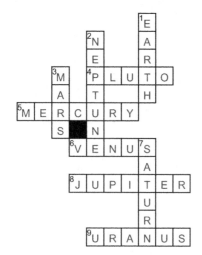

**Across**
4. Was once a planet, now a dwarf planet.
5. This is the smallest planet.
6. The hottest planet in our solar system.
8. It's bigger than any other planet.
9. This planet spins on its side.

**Down**
1. The only planet with life on it.
2. This planet is the furthest from the sun.
3. Also known as the red planet.
7. Most famous for its rings.

**Word Bank**

| | | | |
|---|---|---|---|
| Jupiter | Venus | Mercury | Uranus |
| Mars | Pluto | Neptune | Earth |
| Saturn | | | |

# Play Ball!

**Across**
2. This ball goes BUMP, SET, SPIKE over the net.
5. Athletes use a balance beam.
6. Played with racket and yellow ball.
7. Typically has 18 holes on the course.
8. This ball is orange and played on a court.

**Down**
1. Uses a puck instead of a ball.
3. Played with a bat and ball.
4. Uses a bow and arrow.

**Word Bank**

| | | | |
|---|---|---|---|
| Tennis | Archery | Volleyball | Hockey |
| Gymnastics | Golf | Basketball | Baseball |

# Lettuce Introduce the Veggies

```
M G I W C B Y V D C U C U M B E R
Y P P Y G W P F L A S E V H T A V
H V Z L G B I L J I C U P B L G B
N B D H X P U L J B F I E U A Z X
J B E R G O W T A C E D P N W J E
I I B T D X Q K T M L I P M W T M
E C M A Y K O N I O N V E X L X F
U P O T A T O E S N P L R N Y Q Z
S R B E A N S V C D E Y S F P C Y
O Q S S Z C B U U K L M B B E B Y
H K F Y Q N R Z R V H C N R A Y I
N E F U U G O S I M G O J G S Q W
L F Q L L I C G A U D R L J U G Y
L L S C W H C I F K N C V X K U
E V H F I F O Y A P O P D G L E Y
P L B H K U L I R O M Q B I J X B
X M C I L W I K M B C A R R O T S
```

Beans   Broccoli   Carrots   Corn   Cucumber   Onion   Peas   Peppers
Potatoes

# Man's Best Friends

```
X Z O M X L R F U J
L E N R N B G A S M
I J R A B B I T N O
Z T U R T L E E A U
A P F I F X B Q K S
R B B D I N W Y E E
D Y I O S Y B V U P
V O R L H D C A T P
O N D B U O N V G V
N N R K B G O H Q I
```

Bird   Cat   Dog   Fish   Lizard   Mouse   Rabbit   Snake
Turtle

## Reading is Fun - Sight Words

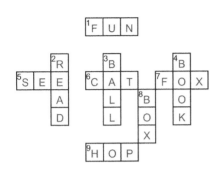

**Across**
1. We had ____ at the park today.
5. I can ____ with my eyes.
6. My ____ is gray with black stripes.
7. The ____ is red and white.
9. The little bunny likes to ____ in the yard.

**Down**
2. I like to ____ in the library.
3. My favorite beach toy is a beach ____.
4. The boy read his ____ after class.
8. Think outside the ____.

**Word Bank**

| | | | |
|---|---|---|---|
| Cat | Fox | Box | Fun |
| Hop | Read | See | Book |
| Ball | | | |

## Under the Sea

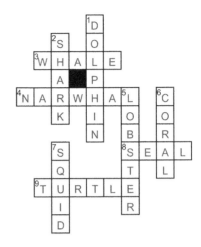

**Across**
3. One species of this mammal is the largest animal on Earth!
4. The unicorn of the sea is a species of whale!
8. This fur-covered sea animal has four flippers.
9. This reptile lays eggs on land but lives in water.

**Down**
1. This sea mammal lives in a group called a pod and uses echolocation like bats!
2. This fish has no bones and can live up to 150 years!
5. This crustacean has five pairs of legs, including claws!
6. The Great Barrier Reef is made of this.
7. This eight-armed creature does not have a backbone!

**Word Bank**

| | | | |
|---|---|---|---|
| Narwhal | Seal | Whale | Coral |
| Turtle | Lobster | Squid | Shark |
| Dolphin | | | |

## On the Farm

```
B O Z P G D F T R C G J X X I V W
F W W J W T L H I A W K H P S M X
M C M R C M Z W S X E T A B C F T
F S H E X N D N Q B K G B L P R E
N L U U C P G G Z C A G S U Z H Z
U M I J G L H S Q H T L O T O M U
P B D U V B A R N I H T V T T D P
V I G P C Q Q R G C M R F E N C E
I Q L T B X W I J K T A E N U A K
D P F Q H D D J F E C M T P F S
M I B R A F H L M N H T O A J T A
M G E S Y S J W E O P O N X I X G
D G H S M N S A E F A R M E R G R
L L H B Q E B T S T J W G L E E A
U X M B D F C H V B M X P S I P I
Z T W M X Z Z E J V A P O L R E N
P F T U E N Y F Z W C O W Q V W O
```

Barn   Chicken   Cow   Farmer   Fence   Grain   Hay   Pig   Tractor

## Outer Space

```
N R S M E T E O R M
G A S T R O N A U T
R C X B S S M R Y K
A A G N P A S T A R
V M U L A O K S U N
I O W J C X I H N M
T O H N E X H E Y Z
Y N O R O C K E T V
X D P L A N E T S E
U R W F K O F R Z A
```

Astronaut   Gravity   Meteor   Moon   Planets   Rocket   Space
Star   Sun

## U.S. Presidents

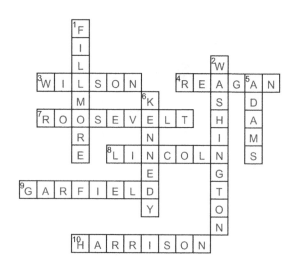

**Across**
3. He kept a flock of sheep at the White House.
4. He was a radio announcer for the Chicago Cubs.
7. This President had a stamp collection.
8. He was the tallest President.
9. This man was the first left-handed President.
10. The only President who studied to become a medical doctor.

**Down**
1. This President's wife started the first White House Library.
2. First President of the United States.
5. First President to live in the White House.
6. He was the first President that was a Boy Scout.

**Word Bank**

| | | | |
|---|---|---|---|
| Reagan | Kennedy | Wilson | Roosevelt |
| Harrison | Lincoln | Washington | Garfield |
| Adams. | Fillmore | | |

## We Walk on Land

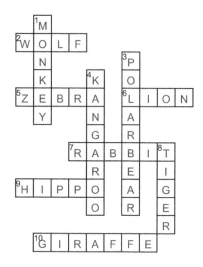

**Across**
2. This animal is the ancestor of our modern dog.
5. This striped animal is closely related to the horse and lives in Africa.
6. Also known as the king of the jungle, this animal's roar can help it jump. be heard up to five miles away!
7. The teeth on this small animal never stop growing.
9. This is the second-largest animal that lives on land..
10. This animal is known for its long neck.

**Down**
1. This fun animal has opposable thumbs, just like us!
3. This species looks white, but its fur is actually transparent!
4. Native to Australia, this land animal has large feet that
8. This striped animal is surprisingly a great swimmer!

**Word Bank**

| | | | |
|---|---|---|---|
| Giraffe | Kangaroo | Tiger | Polar Bear |
| Zebra | Wolf | Hippo | Rabbit |
| Lion | Monkey | | |

## Summer Fun

```
O U W B F M R G T R K L W W R Q S
U R Y I L V E J Q S W I M C I K Y
T S H T E R Q V N I Z E G C S K V
S A C L M D L J P N Z T B N H G V
I L U H O S A N D A L S B Y O O F
D D G F N N N D T D X L A S R U P
E T R P A X M G W T X I E F T U T
K D V N D W O J E C G W A F S N C
Y Z P D E W K D I A Z U K A H L S
W H P A R K H H U Z N C R X J Z X
S X H S U P O P S I C L E I X O S
Q N L O E F N Z C A F D T P K V V
T J V A C A T I O N J Z K L U N Q
H J X A V V U E F W Y D V Q Y T
O S G J L X U J E X P L O R E B E
N D Y T Y E Q Q I C B K C T P I H
C S L B H K R L H X I U K S V S C
```

Explore   Lemonade   Outside   Park   Popsicle   Sandals   Shorts   Swim
Vacation

## U.S. States

```
C A L I F O R N I A
K O B A L C O A H R
F B T P O N H L L H
T J U K R E I E S A
E Q K O I H O H J W
X B J P D E E F O A
A K A L A S K A K I
S R I K A N S A S I
A R I Z O N A S W U
W V N E W Y O R K I
```

Alaska   Arizona   California   Florida   Hawaii   Kansas
New York   Ohio   Texas

# CERTIFICATE
## of completion

### Earned by: